MYplace

FOR SUCCESS

Published by First Place for Health
Galveston, Texas, USA
www.firstplaceforhealth.com
Printed in the USA
© 2018 First Place for Health

Cover & interior design by Lisa Lewis

ISBN 978-1-942425-32-8

To order copies of this book and other First Place for Health products in bulk quantities, please contact us at 800.727.5223 or on our website: www.firstplaceforhealth.com

THIS IS MY PLACE FOR SUCCESS

NAME.......................................

ADDRESS ....

....

PHONE ....

EMAIL ....

FOREWORD

The words "journal" and "journey" are derived from the same root, the French word, "jour," which means "day." This is the perfect description of your First Place for Health wellness journey – daily success, one day at a time, for a lifetime.

There are two habits I believe have transformed my life; having a daily quiet time with God and daily journaling. In those quiet moments spent in the presence of God, He has revealed His great love for me. He has shown me my identity, my calling and my purpose in Christ. He has given me hope and a future. His Word has given me everything I need for life and godliness. It has also transformed my weak and depraved mind into the mind of Christ.

Journaling and tracking have helped me in two ways. First, it has helped me overcome spiritual amnesia. God speaks to me and, if I do not quickly record it, I forget it. I don't intend to forget, but the human mind has limitations. Plus, there is an enemy of our soul whose main goal is to kill, steal and destroy what we receive from God. Therefore, I record my thoughts, feelings and desires and, especially the things God reveals to my heart. Second, journaling helps me keep track of my life. When I lose track of my daily commitments, my life, habits and eating become out of control.

We have designed *My Place for Success* with you in mind. This will be your place for keeping track of your wellness journey in one convenient journal.

• My Nutrition – keeping a daily food tracker of the FP4H Live It Plan is a proved successful tool for creating awareness and avoiding mindless eating. There is space for you to record three meals and a snack. Record in as much detail as is helpful for you.

• My Fitness – when it comes to exercise something is better than nothing and more is better than less. Keep a record of your fitness endeavors and discover how quickly exercise can become a permanent part of your life.

• My Truth – Hiding God's word in your heart is one of the first steps to true transformation.

• My Thoughts - This is the perfect place to record thoughts, feelings, inspirations and reflections on your journey. There is plenty of writing space along with a quote for the day.

You will also notice lots of space for coloring, doodling, scratching, and dreaming. This is your journal. Use it as you see fit, but use it with great joy!

In Christ,

Vicki Heath

_____ / _____ / _____

Date

MY FITNESS
Exercise

_____

_____

_____

_____

✝ MY TRUTH
Scripture Memory Verse

_____

_____

_____

_____

_____

MY NUTRITION

_____

_____

_____

MOOD

_____

_____

_____

MOOD

_____

_____

_____

MOOD

GROUP	FRUITS	VEGETABLES	GRAINS	PROTEIN	DAIRY	HEALTHY OILS & OTHER FATS	WATER & SUPER BEVERAGES
Estimate Total							

What made me happy today?

What positive step did I take for my health?

What intentional step will I take for tomorrow?

THEREFORE, WHETHER YOU

EAT OR DRINK *whatever* YOU **DO** DO IT ALL **FOR THE** *glory* OF **GOD**

_____/_____/_____
Date

MY FITNESS
Exercise

✝ ## MY TRUTH
Scripture Memory Verse

LIVE IT TRACKER

_____

_____

_____

MOOD

_____

_____

_____

MOOD ☺ ☹ ☺

_____

_____

_____

MOOD ☺ ☹ ☺

GROUP	FRUITS	VEGETABLES	GRAINS	PROTEIN	DAIRY	HEALTHY OILS & OTHER FATS	WATER & SUPER BEVERAGES
Estimate Total							

What made me happy today?

What positive step did I take for my health?

What intentional step will I take for tomorrow?

Tell me,
what is it
you plan to do
with your one
wild and
precious
life?

_____/_____/_____
Date

MY FITNESS
Exercise

LIVE IT TRACKER

_____

_____

_____

_____

MOOD

+ # MY TRUTH
Scripture Memory Verse

_____

MOOD

_____

_____

_____

MOOD

GROUP	FRUITS	VEGETABLES	GRAINS	PROTEIN	DAIRY	HEALTHY OILS & OTHER FATS	WATER & SUPER BEVERAGES
Estimate Total							

What made me happy today?

What positive step did I take for my health?

What intentional step will I take for tomorrow?

SPUR
one another on toward
LOVE &
GOOD DEEDS

_____/_____/_____
Date

LIVE IT TRACKER

🏃 MY FITNESS
Exercise

_____

_____

_____

MOOD 🙂 ☹️ 😐

✝ MY TRUTH
Scripture Memory Verse

_____

_____

_____

MOOD 🙂 ☹️ 😐

_____

_____

_____

MOOD 🙂 ☹️ 😐

GROUP	FRUITS	VEGETABLES	GRAINS	PROTEIN	DAIRY	HEALTHY OILS & OTHER FATS	WATER & SUPER BEVERAGES
Estimate Total							

What made me happy today?

What positive step did I take for my health?

What intentional step will I take for tomorrow?

nothing is
IMPOSSIBLE
with God

_____/_____/_____
Date

LIVE IT TRACKER

 MY FITNESS
Exercise

_____

_____

_____

_____

MOOD ☺ ☹ 😐

✝ **MY TRUTH**
Scripture Memory Verse

_____

_____

MOOD ☺ ☹ 😐

_____

_____

MOOD ☺ ☹ 😐

GROUP	FRUITS	VEGETABLES	GRAINS	PROTEIN	DAIRY	HEALTHY OILS & OTHER FATS	WATER & SUPER BEVERAGES
Estimate Total							

What made me happy today?

What positive step did I take for my health?

What intentional step will I take for tomorrow?

Celebrate
—— EVERY ——
VICTORY

_____/_____/_____
Date

MY FITNESS
Exercise

_____

_____

_____

† ## MY TRUTH
Scripture Memory Verse

_____

_____

_____

_____

MY NUTRITION

_____

_____

_____

MOOD

_____

_____

_____

MOOD

_____

_____

_____

MOOD

GROUP	FRUITS	VEGETABLES	GRAINS	PROTEIN	DAIRY	HEALTHY OILS & OTHER FATS	WATER & SUPER BEVERAGES
Estimate Total							

What made me happy today?

What positive step did I take for my health?

What intentional step will I take for tomorrow?

_____

_____

_____

_____

_____

> BUT THANKS BE TO GOD! HE GIVES US THE VICTORY THROUGH OUR LORD JESUS CHRIST.
>
> 1 CORINTHIANS 15:57 NIV

_____

_____

_____

_____

_____

_____

_____

_____

_____

_____

_____

_____

_____

_____

_____

_____

_____

_____ / _____ / _____

Date

MY FITNESS
Exercise

_____

_____

_____

✝ # MY TRUTH
Scripture Memory Verse

_____

_____

_____

_____

LIVE IT TRACKER

_____

_____

_____

MOOD

_____

_____

_____

MOOD

_____

_____

_____

MOOD

GROUP	FRUITS	VEGETABLES	GRAINS	PROTEIN	DAIRY	HEALTHY OILS & OTHER FATS	WATER & SUPER BEVERAGES
Estimate Total							

What made me happy today?

What positive step did I take for my health?

What intentional step will I take for tomorrow?

_____

_____

_____

_____

_____

> I am stronger than
> any challenge that
> comes at me, because
> greater is HE that is
> in me than he that is
> in the world!

_____

_____

_____

_____

_____

_____

_____

_____

_____

_____

_____

_____

_____

_____

_____

_____

_____

_____/_____/_____

Date

MY FITNESS
Exercise

+ ## MY TRUTH
Scripture Memory Verse

LIVE IT TRACKER

MOOD

MOOD

MOOD

GROUP	FRUITS	VEGETABLES	GRAINS	PROTEIN	DAIRY	HEALTHY OILS & OTHER FATS	WATER & SUPER BEVERAGES
Estimate Total							

What made me happy today?

What positive step did I take for my health?

What intentional step will I take for tomorrow?

I WILL GIVE
thanks
TO THE
Lord
WITH MY
Whole Heart
© Valerie M. Kerbat

_____/_____/_____
Date

MY FITNESS
Exercise

_____

_____

_____

✝ # MY TRUTH
Scripture Memory Verse

_____

_____

_____

_____

LIVE IT TRACKER

_____

_____

_____

MOOD

_____

_____

_____

MOOD

_____

_____

_____

MOOD

GROUP	FRUITS	VEGETABLES	GRAINS	PROTEIN	DAIRY	HEALTHY OILS & OTHER FATS	WATER & SUPER BEVERAGES
Estimate Total							

What made me happy today?

What positive step did I take for my health?

What intentional step will I take for tomorrow?

It's About
PROGRESS
Not
Perfection

_____ / _____ / _____

Date

MY FITNESS
Exercise

✝ MY TRUTH
Scripture Memory Verse

LIVE IT TRACKER

MOOD

MOOD

MOOD

GROUP	FRUITS	VEGETABLES	GRAINS	PROTEIN	DAIRY	HEALTHY OILS & OTHER FATS	WATER & SUPER BEVERAGES
Estimate Total							

What made me happy today?

What positive step did I take for my health?

What intentional step will I take for tomorrow?

THE
ONLY BAD
WORKOUT
IS THE ONE
YOU DIDN'T DO

_____/_____/_____

Date

MY FITNESS

Exercise

_____

_____

_____

✝ MY TRUTH

Scripture Memory Verse

_____

_____

_____

_____

MY NUTRITION

_____

_____

_____

MOOD

_____

_____

_____

MOOD

_____

_____

_____

MOOD

GROUP	FRUITS	VEGETABLES	GRAINS	PROTEIN	DAIRY	HEALTHY OILS & OTHER FATS	WATER & SUPER BEVERAGES
Estimate Total							

What made me happy today?

What positive step did I take for my health?

What intentional step will I take for tomorrow?

GREATER IS HE
that is in you
THAN HE THAT IS
in the world.

1 JOHN 4:4

_____/_____/_____
Date

MY FITNESS
Exercise

_____
_____
_____

✝ MY TRUTH
Scripture Memory Verse

_____
_____
_____
_____
_____

LIVE IT TRACKER

_____
_____
_____

MOOD 🙂 🙁 😐

_____
_____
_____

MOOD 🙂 🙁 😐

_____
_____
_____

MOOD 🙂 🙁 😐

GROUP	FRUITS	VEGETABLES	GRAINS	PROTEIN	DAIRY	HEALTHY OILS & OTHER FATS	WATER & SUPER BEVERAGES
Estimate Total							

What made me happy today?

What positive step did I take for my health?

What intentional step will I take for tomorrow?

BE
STRONGER
THAN YOUR
EXCUSES

_____/_____/_____
Date

MY FITNESS
Exercise

_____

_____

_____

MY TRUTH
Scripture Memory Verse

_____

_____

_____

_____

_____

LIVE IT TRACKER

_____

_____

_____

MOOD

_____

_____

_____

MOOD

_____

_____

_____

MOOD

GROUP	FRUITS	VEGETABLES	GRAINS	PROTEIN	DAIRY	HEALTHY OILS & OTHER FATS	WATER & SUPER BEVERAGES
Estimate Total							

What made me happy today?

What positive step did I take for my health?

What intentional step will I take for tomorrow?

Rejoice *always,*

PRAY *continually*

give thanks in all circumstances;

for this is God's will for you in *Christ Jesus.*

1 Thessalonians 5:16-18

_____/_____/_____

Date

🏃 MY FITNESS
Exercise

_____

_____

_____

✝ MY TRUTH
Scripture Memory Verse

_____

_____

_____

_____

LIVE IT TRACKER

_____

_____

_____

MOOD

_____

_____

_____

MOOD

_____

_____

_____

MOOD

GROUP	FRUITS	VEGETABLES	GRAINS	PROTEIN	DAIRY	HEALTHY OILS & OTHER FATS	WATER & SUPER BEVERAGES
Estimate Total							

What made me happy today?

What positive step did I take for my health?

What intentional step will I take for tomorrow?

_____

_____

_____

_____

_____

_____

_____

_____

_____

_____

_____

_____

_____

_____

_____

_____

_____

_____

_____

_____

_____

_____

_____

_____

_____/_____/_____
Date

MY FITNESS
Exercise

MY TRUTH
Scripture Memory Verse

LIVE IT TRACKER

MOOD

MOOD

MOOD

GROUP	FRUITS	VEGETABLES	GRAINS	PROTEIN	DAIRY	HEALTHY OILS & OTHER FATS	WATER & SUPER BEVERAGES
Estimate Total							

What made me happy today?

What positive step did I take for my health?

What intentional step will I take for tomorrow?

WOUNDS FROM A
SINCERE FRIEND
ARE BETTER THAN
MANY FROM AN
KISSES ENEMY
Proverbs 27:6

_____/_____/_____
Date

MY FITNESS
Exercise

_____

_____

_____

✝ MY TRUTH
Scripture Memory Verse

_____

_____

_____

_____

MY NUTRITION

_____

_____

_____

MOOD

_____

_____

_____

MOOD

_____

_____

_____

MOOD

GROUP	FRUITS	VEGETABLES	GRAINS	PROTEIN	DAIRY	HEALTHY OILS & OTHER FATS	WATER & SUPER BEVERAGES
Estimate Total							

What made me happy today?

What positive step did I take for my health?

What intentional step will I take for tomorrow?

Do The Next Right Thing

www.firstplace4health.com

_____ / _____ / _____

Date

LIVE IT TRACKER

🏃 MY FITNESS
Exercise

_____

_____

_____

MOOD 🙂 🙁 😐

✝ MY TRUTH
Scripture Memory Verse

_____

_____

_____

_____

MOOD 🙂 🙁 😐

_____

_____

MOOD 🙂 🙁 😐

GROUP	FRUITS	VEGETABLES	GRAINS	PROTEIN	DAIRY	HEALTHY OILS & OTHER FATS	WATER & SUPER BEVERAGES
Estimate Total							

What made me happy today?

What positive step did I take for my health?

What intentional step will I take for tomorrow?

_____

_____

_____

_____

_____

Obedience is God's
LOVE
Language

www.FirstPlace4Health.com

_____

_____

_____

_____

_____

_____

_____

_____

_____

_____

_____

_____

_____

_____

_____

_____

_____/_____/_____
Date

🏃 MY FITNESS
Exercise

LIVE IT TRACKER

_____

_____

_____

_____

MOOD 🙂 ☹️ 😐

_____

✝ MY TRUTH
Scripture Memory Verse

_____

_____

_____

_____

_____

MOOD 🙂 ☹️ 😐

_____

_____

_____

MOOD 🙂 ☹️ 😐

GROUP	FRUITS	VEGETABLES	GRAINS	PROTEIN	DAIRY	HEALTHY OILS & OTHER FATS	WATER & SUPER BEVERAGES
Estimate Total							

What made me happy today?

What positive step did I take for my health?

What intentional step will I take for tomorrow?

WHEN IT COMES TO EXERCISE, SOMETHING IS BETTER THAN NOTHING AND MORE IS BETTER THAN LESS.

_____/_____/_____

Date

🏃 MY FITNESS
Exercise

_____

_____

_____

_____

✝ MY TRUTH
Scripture Memory Verse

_____

_____

_____

_____

LIVE IT TRACKER

_____

_____

_____

_____

MOOD

_____

_____

_____

MOOD 😊 ☹ 😐

_____

_____

_____

_____

MOOD 😊 ☹ 😐

GROUP	FRUITS	VEGETABLES	GRAINS	PROTEIN	DAIRY	HEALTHY OILS & OTHER FATS	WATER & SUPER BEVERAGES
Estimate Total							

What made me happy today?

What positive step did I take for my health?

What intentional step will I take for tomorrow?

_____

_____

_____

_____

Setbacks are temporary; it's quitting that makes it permanent.

_____

_____

_____

_____

_____

_____

_____

_____

_____

_____

_____

_____

_____

_____

_____

_____

_____

_____

_____

_____ / _____ / _____

Date

MY FITNESS
Exercise

✝ MY TRUTH
Scripture Memory Verse

LIVE IT TRACKER

MOOD ☺ ☹ 😐

MOOD ☺ ☹ 😐

MOOD ☺ ☹ 😐

GROUP	FRUITS	VEGETABLES	GRAINS	PROTEIN	DAIRY	HEALTHY OILS & OTHER FATS	WATER & SUPER BEVERAGES
Estimate Total							

What made me happy today?

What positive step did I take for my health?

What intentional step will I take for tomorrow?

> If it's important to you,
> you will find a way.
> If it's not, you will
> find an excuse.

_____/_____/_____

Date

MY FITNESS
Exercise

_____

_____

_____

✝ MY TRUTH
Scripture Memory Verse

_____

_____

_____

_____

MY NUTRITION

_____

_____

_____

MOOD

_____

_____

_____

MOOD 😊 ☹️ 😐

_____

_____

_____

MOOD 😊 ☹️ 😐

GROUP	FRUITS	VEGETABLES	GRAINS	PROTEIN	DAIRY	HEALTHY OILS & OTHER FATS	WATER & SUPER BEVERAGES
➊ Estimate Total							

What made me happy today?

What positive step did I take for my health?

What intentional step will I take for tomorrow?

Prayer
is the bridge
between panic &
peace

_____/_____/_____
Date

MY FITNESS
Exercise

✝ MY TRUTH
Scripture Memory Verse

LIVE IT TRACKER

MOOD

MOOD 😊 ☹️ 😐

MOOD 😊 ☹️ 😐

GROUP	FRUITS	VEGETABLES	GRAINS	PROTEIN	DAIRY	HEALTHY OILS & OTHER FATS	WATER & SUPER BEVERAGES
Estimate Total							

What made me happy today?

What positive step did I take for my health?

What intentional step will I take for tomorrow?

When God gives you a
new beginning,
don't repeat the
old mistakes

_____/_____/_____
Date

MY FITNESS
Exercise

✝ MY TRUTH
Scripture Memory Verse

LIVE IT TRACKER

MOOD

MOOD

MOOD

GROUP	FRUITS	VEGETABLES	GRAINS	PROTEIN	DAIRY	HEALTHY OILS & OTHER FATS	WATER & SUPER BEVERAGES
Estimate Total							

What made me happy today?

What positive step did I take for my health?

What intentional step will I take for tomorrow?

Moving
CHANGES
Everything

_____/_____/_____
Date

MY FITNESS
Exercise

✝ **MY TRUTH**
Scripture Memory Verse

LIVE IT TRACKER

_____

_____

MOOD

_____

_____

MOOD

_____

_____

MOOD

GROUP	FRUITS	VEGETABLES	GRAINS	PROTEIN	DAIRY	HEALTHY OILS & OTHER FATS	WATER & SUPER BEVERAGES
Estimate Total							

What made me happy today?

What positive step did I take for my health?

What intentional step will I take for tomorrow?

Put Your
FAITH
in Action

____/____/____
Date

MY FITNESS
Exercise

_____
_____
_____

✝ # MY TRUTH
Scripture Memory Verse

_____
_____
_____
_____

MY NUTRITION

_____
_____
_____

MOOD ☺ ☹ 😐

_____
_____

MOOD ☺ ☹ 😐

_____
_____

MOOD ☺ ☹ 😐

GROUP	FRUITS	VEGETABLES	GRAINS	PROTEIN	DAIRY	HEALTHY OILS & OTHER FATS	WATER & SUPER BEVERAGES
Estimate Total							

What made me happy today?

What positive step did I take for my health?

What intentional step will I take for tomorrow?

Small steps
lead to
big changes

_____ / _____ / _____

Date

MY FITNESS
Exercise

LIVE IT TRACKER

MY TRUTH
Scripture Memory Verse

MOOD

MOOD

MOOD

GROUP	FRUITS	VEGETABLES	GRAINS	PROTEIN	DAIRY	HEALTHY OILS & OTHER FATS	WATER & SUPER BEVERAGES
Estimate Total							

What made me happy today?

What positive step did I take for my health?

What intentional step will I take for tomorrow?

_____

_____

_____

_____

_____

I am stronger than
any challenge that
comes at me, because
greater is HE that is
in me than he that is
in the world!

_____

_____

_____

_____

_____

_____

_____

_____

_____

_____

_____

_____

_____

_____

_____

_____/_____/_____
Date

🏃 MY FITNESS
Exercise

_____
_____
_____

✝ MY TRUTH
Scripture Memory Verse

_____
_____
_____

LIVE IT TRACKER

_____
_____
_____
_____

MOOD

_____
_____
_____

MOOD

_____
_____
_____

MOOD

GROUP	FRUITS	VEGETABLES	GRAINS	PROTEIN	DAIRY	HEALTHY OILS & OTHER FATS	WATER & SUPER BEVERAGES
Estimate Total							

What made me happy today?

What positive step did I take for my health?

What intentional step will I take for tomorrow?

I WILL GIVE thanks TO THE Lord WITH MY Whole Heart

© Valerie McKeehan

_____/_____/_____
Date

🏃 MY FITNESS
Exercise

_____

_____

_____

✝ MY TRUTH
Scripture Memory Verse

_____

_____

_____

_____

LIVE IT TRACKER

_____

_____

_____

_____

MOOD 😊 🙁 😐

_____

_____

_____

MOOD 😊 🙁 😐

_____

_____

_____

MOOD 😊 🙁 😐

GROUP	FRUITS	VEGETABLES	GRAINS	PROTEIN	DAIRY	HEALTHY OILS & OTHER FATS	WATER & SUPER BEVERAGES
Estimate Total							

What made me happy today?

What positive step did I take for my health?

What intentional step will I take for tomorrow?

It's About
PROGRESS
Not
Perfection

_____/_____/_____

Date

MY FITNESS
Exercise

✝ MY TRUTH
Scripture Memory Verse

LIVE IT TRACKER

MOOD

MOOD

MOOD

GROUP	FRUITS	VEGETABLES	GRAINS	PROTEIN	DAIRY	HEALTHY OILS & OTHER FATS	WATER & SUPER BEVERAGES
Estimate Total							

What made me happy today?

What positive step did I take for my health?

What intentional step will I take for tomorrow?

_____

_____

_____

_____

_____

THE
ONLY BAD
WORKOUT
IS THE ONE
YOU DIDN'T DO

_____

_____

_____

_____

_____

_____

_____

_____

_____

_____

_____

_____

_____

_____

_____

_____

_____

_____ / _____ / _____

Date

MY FITNESS
Exercise

MY NUTRITION

MOOD

✝ ## MY TRUTH
Scripture Memory Verse

MOOD 🙂 🙁 😐

MOOD 🙂 🙁 😐

GROUP	FRUITS	VEGETABLES	GRAINS	PROTEIN	DAIRY	HEALTHY OILS & OTHER FATS	WATER & SUPER BEVERAGES
Estimate Total							

What made me happy today?

What positive step did I take for my health?

What intentional step will I take for tomorrow?

GREATER IS HE
that is in you
THAN HE THAT IS
in the world.

1 JOHN 4:4

_____/_____/_____
Date

MY FITNESS
Exercise

LIVE IT TRACKER

MOOD  😊 ☹️ 😐

✝ MY TRUTH
Scripture Memory Verse

MOOD 😊 ☹️ 😐

MOOD 😊 ☹️ 😐

GROUP	FRUITS	VEGETABLES	GRAINS	PROTEIN	DAIRY	HEALTHY OILS & OTHER FATS	WATER & SUPER BEVERAGES
Estimate Total							

What made me happy today?

What positive step did I take for my health?

What intentional step will I take for tomorrow?

_____

_____

_____

_____

_____

_____

_____

_____

_____

_____

_____

_____

_____

_____

_____

_____

_____

_____

_____

_____

_____

_____

_____

_____

_____/_____/_____
Date

🏃 MY FITNESS
Exercise

_____

_____

_____

✝ MY TRUTH
Scripture Memory Verse

_____

_____

_____

_____

LIVE IT TRACKER

_____

_____

_____

_____

MOOD 🙂 🙁 😐

_____

_____

_____

MOOD 🙂 🙁 😐

_____

_____

_____

MOOD 🙂 🙁 😐

GROUP	FRUITS	VEGETABLES	GRAINS	PROTEIN	DAIRY	HEALTHY OILS & OTHER FATS	WATER & SUPER BEVERAGES
Estimate Total							

What made me happy today?

What positive step did I take for my health?

What intentional step will I take for tomorrow?

Rejoice always,
PRAY continually
give thanks in all circumstances;
for this is God's will for you in *Christ Jesus.*

1 Thessalonians 5:16-18

_____/_____/_____

Date

MY FITNESS

Exercise

_____

_____

_____

✝ MY TRUTH

Scripture Memory Verse

_____

_____

_____

_____

LIVE IT TRACKER

_____

_____

_____

MOOD

_____

_____

_____

MOOD

_____

_____

_____

MOOD

GROUP	FRUITS	VEGETABLES	GRAINS	PROTEIN	DAIRY	HEALTHY OILS & OTHER FATS	WATER & SUPER BEVERAGES
Estimate Total							

What made me happy today?

What positive step did I take for my health?

What intentional step will I take for tomorrow?

A CHEERFUL HEART IS GOOD MEDICINE -proverbs 17:22

_____

_____

_____

_____

_____

_____

_____

_____

_____

_____

_____

_____

_____

_____

_____

_____

_____

_____

_____

_____

_____

_____

_____

_____

_____ / _____ / _____

Date

🏃 MY FITNESS
Exercise

✝ MY TRUTH
Scripture Memory Verse

LIVE IT TRACKER

MOOD

MOOD

MOOD

GROUP	FRUITS	VEGETABLES	GRAINS	PROTEIN	DAIRY	HEALTHY OILS & OTHER FATS	WATER & SUPER BEVERAGES
Estimate Total							

What made me happy today?

What positive step did I take for my health?

What intentional step will I take for tomorrow?

WOUNDS FROM A
SINCERE FRIEND
ARE BETTER THAN
MANY FROM AN
KISSES ENEMY
Proverbs 27:6

_____/_____/_____
Date

MY FITNESS
Exercise

_____

_____

_____

✝ # MY TRUTH
Scripture Memory Verse

_____

_____

_____

_____

MY NUTRITION

_____

_____

_____

_____

MOOD

_____

_____

_____

MOOD 🙂 🙁 😐

_____

_____

_____

MOOD 🙂 🙁 😐

GROUP	FRUITS	VEGETABLES	GRAINS	PROTEIN	DAIRY	HEALTHY OILS & OTHER FATS	WATER & SUPER BEVERAGES
Estimate Total							

What made me happy today?

What positive step did I take for my health?

What intentional step will I take for tomorrow?

Do The Next Right Thing

www.firstplace4health.com

_____/_____/_____

Date

MY FITNESS
Exercise

✝ MY TRUTH
Scripture Memory Verse

LIVE IT TRACKER

_____

_____

_____

MOOD

_____

_____

_____

MOOD ☺ ☹ 😐

_____

_____

_____

MOOD ☺ ☹ 😐

GROUP	FRUITS	VEGETABLES	GRAINS	PROTEIN	DAIRY	HEALTHY OILS & OTHER FATS	WATER & SUPER BEVERAGES
Estimate Total							

What made me happy today?

What positive step did I take for my health?

What intentional step will I take for tomorrow?

Obedience is God's
LOVE
Language

www.FirstPlaceHealth.com

_____/_____/_____
Date

MY FITNESS
Exercise

_____

_____

_____

✝ # MY TRUTH
Scripture Memory Verse

_____

_____

_____

_____

LIVE IT TRACKER

_____

_____

_____

MOOD

_____

_____

MOOD ☺ ☹ 😐

_____

_____

_____

MOOD ☺ ☹ 😐

GROUP	FRUITS	VEGETABLES	GRAINS	PROTEIN	DAIRY	HEALTHY OILS & OTHER FATS	WATER & SUPER BEVERAGES
Estimate Total							

What made me happy today?

What positive step did I take for my health?

What intentional step will I take for tomorrow?

WHEN IT COMES TO EXERCISE, SOMETHING IS BETTER THAN NOTHING AND MORE IS BETTER THAN LESS.

_____ / _____ / _____
Date

MY FITNESS
Exercise

_____

_____

_____

✝ MY TRUTH
Scripture Memory Verse

_____

_____

_____

_____

LIVE IT TRACKER

_____

_____

_____

MOOD 🙂 🙁 😐

_____

_____

_____

MOOD 🙂 🙁 😐

_____

_____

_____

MOOD 🙂 🙁 😐

GROUP	FRUITS	VEGETABLES	GRAINS	PROTEIN	DAIRY	HEALTHY OILS & OTHER FATS	WATER & SUPER BEVERAGES
Estimate Total							

What made me happy today?

What positive step did I take for my health?

What intentional step will I take for tomorrow?

Setbacks are temporary; it's quitting that makes it permanent.

_____/_____/_____
Date

MY FITNESS
Exercise

_____

_____

_____

✝ # MY TRUTH
Scripture Memory Verse

_____

_____

_____

_____

LIVE IT TRACKER

_____

_____

_____

MOOD 🙂 🙁 😐

_____

_____

_____

MOOD 🙂 🙁 😐

_____

_____

_____

MOOD

GROUP	FRUITS	VEGETABLES	GRAINS	PROTEIN	DAIRY	HEALTHY OILS & OTHER FATS	WATER & SUPER BEVERAGES
Estimate Total							

What made me happy today?

What positive step did I take for my health?

What intentional step will I take for tomorrow?

If it's important to you,
you will find a way.
If it's not, you will
find an excuse.

_____/_____/_____
Date

MY FITNESS
Exercise

_____

_____

_____

+ # MY TRUTH
Scripture Memory Verse

_____

_____

_____

_____

MY NUTRITION

_____

_____

_____

MOOD 😊 ☹️ 😐

_____

_____

_____

MOOD 😊 ☹️ 😐

_____

_____

_____

MOOD 😊 ☹️ 😐

GROUP	FRUITS	VEGETABLES	GRAINS	PROTEIN	DAIRY	HEALTHY OILS & OTHER FATS	WATER & SUPER BEVERAGES
Estimate Total							

What made me happy today?

What positive step did I take for my health?

What intentional step will I take for tomorrow?

THEREFORE, WHETHER YOU

EAT OR
DRINK
whatever you DO
DO IT ALL
FOR THE *glory*
OF GOD

_____/_____/_____
Date

![running person icon] **MY FITNESS**
Exercise

_____

_____

_____

✝ **MY TRUTH**
Scripture Memory Verse

_____

_____

_____

_____

_____

LIVE IT TRACKER

_____

_____

_____

_____

MOOD 😊 ☹️ 😐

_____

_____

_____

_____

MOOD 😊 ☹️ 😐

_____

_____

_____

MOOD 😊 ☹️ 😐

GROUP	FRUITS	VEGETABLES	GRAINS	PROTEIN	DAIRY	HEALTHY OILS & OTHER FATS	WATER & SUPER BEVERAGES
Estimate Total							

What made me happy today?

What positive step did I take for my health?

What intentional step will I take for tomorrow?

Tell me,
what is it
you plan to do
with your one
wild and
precious
life?

_____/_____/_____
Date

![runner icon] **MY FITNESS**
Exercise

✝ **MY TRUTH**
Scripture Memory Verse

LIVE IT TRACKER

_____

_____

_____

MOOD

_____

_____

_____

MOOD

_____

_____

_____

MOOD

GROUP	FRUITS	VEGETABLES	GRAINS	PROTEIN	DAIRY	HEALTHY OILS & OTHER FATS	WATER & SUPER BEVERAGES
Estimate Total							

What made me happy today?

What positive step did I take for my health?

What intentional step will I take for tomorrow?

SPUR
one another on toward
LOVE &
GOOD DEEDS

_____ / _____ / _____
Date

 MY FITNESS
Exercise

_____

_____

_____

✝ **MY TRUTH**
Scripture Memory Verse

_____

_____

_____

_____

LIVE IT TRACKER

_____

_____

_____

MOOD 😊 😞 😐

_____

_____

_____

MOOD 😊 😞 😐

_____

_____

_____

MOOD 😊 😞 😐

GROUP	FRUITS	VEGETABLES	GRAINS	PROTEIN	DAIRY	HEALTHY OILS & OTHER FATS	WATER & SUPER BEVERAGES
Estimate Total							

What made me happy today?

What positive step did I take for my health?

What intentional step will I take for tomorrow?

_____
_____
_____
_____

nothing is IMPOSSIBLE with God

_____
_____
_____
_____
_____
_____
_____
_____
_____
_____
_____
_____
_____
_____
_____
_____

_____
_____
_____
_____
_____

_____/_____/_____
Date

MY FITNESS
Exercise

LIVE IT TRACKER

MOOD 🙂 🙁 😐

✝ MY TRUTH
Scripture Memory Verse

MOOD 🙂 🙁 😐

MOOD 🙂 🙁 😐

GROUP	FRUITS	VEGETABLES	GRAINS	PROTEIN	DAIRY	HEALTHY OILS & OTHER FATS	WATER & SUPER BEVERAGES
Estimate Total							

What made me happy today?

What positive step did I take for my health?

What intentional step will I take for tomorrow?

Celebrate

——— EVERY ———

VICTORY

_____ / _____ / _____
Date

🏃 MY FITNESS
Exercise

_____

_____

_____

✝ MY TRUTH
Scripture Memory Verse

_____

_____

_____

_____

MY NUTRITION

_____

_____

_____

MOOD ☺ ☹ 😐

_____

_____

_____

MOOD ☺ ☹ 😐

_____

_____

_____

MOOD ☺ ☹ 😐

GROUP	FRUITS	VEGETABLES	GRAINS	PROTEIN	DAIRY	HEALTHY OILS & OTHER FATS	WATER & SUPER BEVERAGES
Estimate Total							

What made me happy today?

What positive step did I take for my health?

What intentional step will I take for tomorrow?

_____

_____

_____

_____

_____

> BUT THANKS BE TO GOD! HE GIVES US THE VICTORY THROUGH OUR LORD JESUS CHRIST.
>
> 1 CORINTHIANS 15:57 NIV

_____

_____

_____

_____

_____

_____

_____

_____

_____

_____

_____

_____

_____

_____

_____

_____

_____/_____/_____

Date

MY FITNESS
Exercise

✝ MY TRUTH
Scripture Memory Verse

LIVE IT TRACKER

MOOD

MOOD

MOOD

GROUP	FRUITS	VEGETABLES	GRAINS	PROTEIN	DAIRY	HEALTHY OILS & OTHER FATS	WATER & SUPER BEVERAGES
Estimate Total							

What made me happy today?

What positive step did I take for my health?

What intentional step will I take for tomorrow?

I am stronger than any challenge that comes at me, because greater is HE that is in me than he that is in the world!

_____/_____/_____

Date

MY FITNESS

Exercise

✝ MY TRUTH

Scripture Memory Verse

LIVE IT TRACKER

MOOD

MOOD

MOOD

GROUP	FRUITS	VEGETABLES	GRAINS	PROTEIN	DAIRY	HEALTHY OILS & OTHER FATS	WATER & SUPER BEVERAGES
Estimate Total							

What made me happy today?

What positive step did I take for my health?

What intentional step will I take for tomorrow?

I WILL GIVE thanks TO THE Lord WITH MY Whole Heart

© Valerie McKeehan

_____

_____

_____

_____

_____

_____

_____

_____

_____

_____

_____

_____

_____

_____

_____

_____

_____

_____

_____

_____/_____/_____
Date

MY FITNESS
Exercise

LIVE IT TRACKER

MOOD 😊 ☹️ 😐

✝ # MY TRUTH
Scripture Memory Verse

MOOD 😊 ☹️ 😐

MOOD 😊 ☹️ 😐

GROUP	FRUITS	VEGETABLES	GRAINS	PROTEIN	DAIRY	HEALTHY OILS & OTHER FATS	WATER & SUPER BEVERAGES
Estimate Total							

What made me happy today?

What positive step did I take for my health?

What intentional step will I take for tomorrow?

It's About
PROGRESS
Not
Perfection

_____/_____/_____
Date

MY FITNESS
Exercise

_____

_____

_____

✝ MY TRUTH
Scripture Memory Verse

_____

_____

_____

_____

LIVE IT TRACKER

_____

_____

_____

MOOD

_____

_____

_____

MOOD

_____

_____

_____

MOOD

GROUP	FRUITS	VEGETABLES	GRAINS	PROTEIN	DAIRY	HEALTHY OILS & OTHER FATS	WATER & BEVERA...
Estimate Total							

What made me happy today?

What positive step did I take for my health?

What intentional step will I take for tomorrow?

THE
ONLY BAD
WORKOUT
IS THE ONE
YOU DIDN'T DO

_____/_____/_____

Date

MY FITNESS
Exercise

_____

_____

_____

_____

+ MY TRUTH
Scripture Memory Verse

_____

_____

_____

_____

MY NUTRITION

_____

_____

MOOD

_____

_____

_____

MOOD

_____

_____

MOOD

GROUP	FRUITS	VEGETABLES	GRAINS	PROTEIN	DAIRY	HEALTHY OILS & OTHER FATS	WATER & SUPER BEVERAGES
Estimate Total							

What made me happy today?

What positive step did I take for my health?

What intentional step will I take for tomorrow?

_____
_____
_____
_____
_____

GREATER IS HE
that is in you
THAN HE THAT IS
in the world.

1 JOHN 4:4

_____
_____
_____
_____
_____
_____
_____
_____
_____
_____
_____
_____
_____

_____
_____
_____
_____
_____

_____ / _____ / _____

Date

🏃 MY FITNESS
Exercise

_____

_____

_____

✝ MY TRUTH
Scripture Memory Verse

_____

_____

_____

_____

LIVE IT TRACKER

_____

_____

_____

MOOD

_____

_____

_____

MOOD

_____

_____

_____

MOOD

GROUP	FRUITS	VEGETABLES	GRAINS	PROTEIN	DAIRY	HEALTHY OILS & OTHER FATS	WATER & SUPE BEVERAGES
Estimate Total							

What made me happy today?

What positive step did I take for my health?

What intentional step will I take for tomorrow?

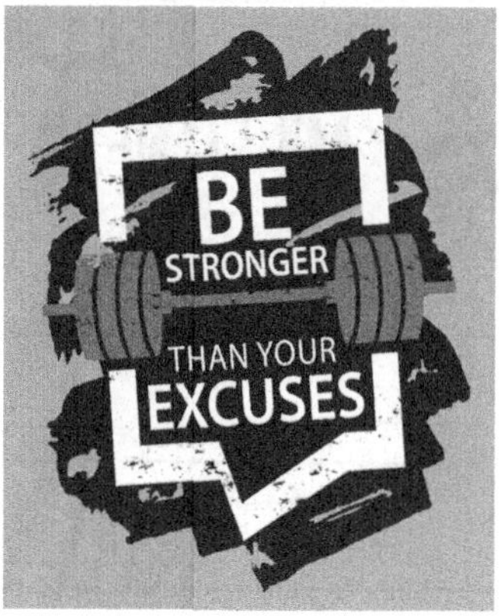
BE
STRONGER
THAN YOUR
EXCUSES

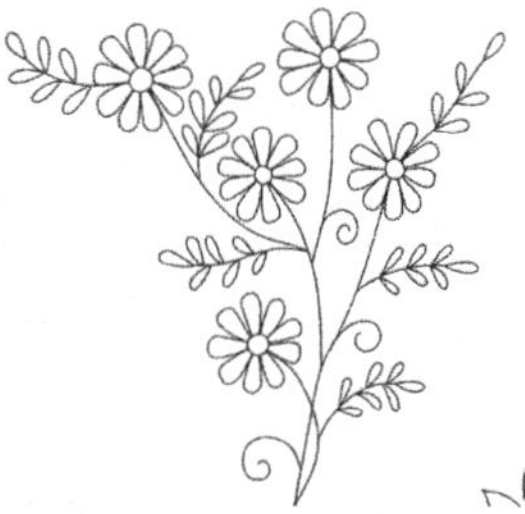

_____/_____/_____
Date

![runner icon] **MY FITNESS**
Exercise

_____

_____

_____

_____

✝ **MY TRUTH**
Scripture Memory Verse

_____

_____

_____

_____

LIVE IT TRACKER

_____

_____

_____

_____

MOOD

_____

_____

_____

_____

MOOD 😊 ☹ 😐

_____

_____

_____

_____

MOOD 😊 ☹ 😐

GROUP	FRUITS	VEGETABLES	GRAINS	PROTEIN	DAIRY	HEALTHY OILS & OTHER FATS	WATER & SUPER BEVERAGES
Estimate Total							

What made me happy today?

What positive step did I take for my health?

What intentional step will I take for tomorrow?

Rejoice always,

PRAY continually

give thanks in all circumstances;

for this is God's will for you in Christ Jesus.

1 Thessalonians 5:16-18

_____ / _____ / _____

Date

🏃 MY FITNESS
Exercise

✝ MY TRUTH
Scripture Memory Verse

LIVE IT TRACKER

_____

_____

_____

MOOD

_____

_____

_____

MOOD

_____

_____

_____

MOOD

GROUP	FRUITS	VEGETABLES	GRAINS	PROTEIN	DAIRY	HEALTHY OILS & OTHER FATS	WATER & SUPER BEVERAGES
Estimate Total							

What made me happy today?

What positive step did I take for my health?

What intentional step will I take for tomorrow?

A CHEERFUL HEART IS GOOD MEDICINE
-proverbs 17:22

_____/_____/_____
Date

MY FITNESS
Exercise

MY NUTRITION

_____

_____

_____

_____

MOOD

✝ MY TRUTH
Scripture Memory Verse

_____

_____

MOOD

_____

_____

_____

MOOD

GROUP	FRUITS	VEGETABLES	GRAINS	PROTEIN	DAIRY	HEALTHY OILS & OTHER FATS	WATER & SUPER BEVERAGES
Estimate Total							

What made me happy today?

What positive step did I take for my health?

What intentional step will I take for tomorrow?

Do The Next Right Thing

www.firstplace4health.com

_____/_____/_____
Date

🏃 MY FITNESS
Exercise

_____

_____

_____

✝ MY TRUTH
Scripture Memory Verse

_____

_____

_____

_____

LIVE IT TRACKER

_____

_____

_____

MOOD ☺ ☹ 😐

_____

_____

_____

MOOD ☺ ☹ 😐

_____

_____

_____

MOOD ☺ ☹ 😐

GROUP	FRUITS	VEGETABLES	GRAINS	PROTEIN	DAIRY	HEALTHY OILS & OTHER FATS	WATER & SUPER BEVERAGES
Estimate Total							

What made me happy today?

What positive step did I take for my health?

What intentional step will I take for tomorrow?

Obedience is God's
LOVE
Language

_____/_____/_____

Date

MY FITNESS
Exercise

LIVE IT TRACKER

MOOD 🙂 🙁 😐

✝ MY TRUTH
Scripture Memory Verse

MOOD 🙂 🙁 😐

MOOD 🙂 🙁 😐

GROUP	FRUITS	VEGETABLES	GRAINS	PROTEIN	DAIRY	HEALTHY OILS & OTHER FATS	WATER & SUPER BEVERAGES
Estimate Total							

What made me happy today?

What positive step did I take for my health?

What intentional step will I take for tomorrow?

WHEN IT COMES TO EXERCISE, SOMETHING IS BETTER THAN NOTHING AND MORE IS BETTER THAN LESS.

_____ / _____ / _____

Date

MY FITNESS
Exercise

_____

_____

_____

✝ MY TRUTH
Scripture Memory Verse

_____

_____

_____

_____

LIVE IT TRACKER

_____

_____

_____

_____

MOOD

_____

_____

_____

_____

MOOD

_____

_____

_____

MOOD

GROUP	FRUITS	VEGETABLES	GRAINS	PROTEIN	DAIRY	HEALTHY OILS & OTHER FATS	WATER & SUPER BEVERAGES
Estimate Total							

What made me happy today?

What positive step did I take for my health?

What intentional step will I take for tomorrow?

Setbacks are temporary; it's quitting that makes it permanent.

_____/_____/_____
Date

🏃 MY FITNESS
Exercise

_____

_____

_____

✝ MY TRUTH
Scripture Memory Verse

_____

_____

_____

_____

LIVE IT TRACKER

_____

_____

_____

MOOD 🙂 🙁 😐

_____

_____

_____

MOOD 🙂 🙁 😐

_____

_____

_____

MOOD

GROUP	FRUITS	VEGETABLES	GRAINS	PROTEIN	DAIRY	HEALTHY OILS & OTHER FATS	WATER & SUPE BEVERAGES
Estimate Total							

What made me happy today?

What positive step did I take for my health?

What intentional step will I take for tomorrow?

If it's important to you,
you will find a way.
If it's not, you will
find an excuse.

_____/_____/_____

Date

MY FITNESS

Exercise

_____

_____

_____

_____

✝ MY TRUTH

Scripture Memory Verse

_____

_____

_____

_____

_____

MY NUTRITION

_____

_____

_____

MOOD

_____

_____

_____

_____

MOOD

_____

_____

_____

MOOD

GROUP	FRUITS	VEGETABLES	GRAINS	PROTEIN	DAIRY	HEALTHY OILS & OTHER FATS	WATER & SUPE BEVERAGES
Estimate Total							

What made me happy today?

What positive step did I take for my health?

What intentional step will I take for tomorrow?

THEREFORE, WHETHER YOU

EAT OR DRINK
whatever you **DO**
DO IT ALL
FOR THE *glory*
of **GOD**

_____ / _____ / _____
Date

MY FITNESS
Exercise

MY TRUTH
Scripture Memory Verse

LIVE IT TRACKER

MOOD

MOOD

MOOD

GROUP	FRUITS	VEGETABLES	GRAINS	PROTEIN	DAIRY	HEALTHY OILS & OTHER FATS	WATER & SUPER BEVERAGES
Estimate Total							

What made me happy today?

What positive step did I take for my health?

What intentional step will I take for tomorrow?

**Tell me,
what is it
you plan to do
with your one
wild and
precious
life?**

_____/_____/_____
Date

MY FITNESS
Exercise

✝ MY TRUTH
Scripture Memory Verse

LIVE IT TRACKER

MOOD

MOOD

MOOD

GROUP	FRUITS	VEGETABLES	GRAINS	PROTEIN	DAIRY	HEALTHY OILS & OTHER FATS	WATER & SUPER BEVERAGES
Estimate Total							

What made me happy today?

What positive step did I take for my health?

What intentional step will I take for tomorrow?

SPUR
one another on toward
LOVE &
GOOD DEEDS

_____/_____/_____
Date

🏃 MY FITNESS
Exercise

_____

_____

_____

✝ MY TRUTH
Scripture Memory Verse

_____

_____

_____

_____

LIVE IT TRACKER

_____

_____

_____

MOOD 😊 ☹ 😐

_____

_____

_____

MOOD 😊 ☹ 😐

_____

_____

_____

MOOD 😊 ☹ 😐

GROUP	FRUITS	VEGETABLES	GRAINS	PROTEIN	DAIRY	HEALTHY OILS & OTHER FATS	WATER & SUPER BEVERAGES
Estimate Total							

What made me happy today?

What positive step did I take for my health?

What intentional step will I take for tomorrow?

nothing is
IMPOSSIBLE
with God

_____/_____/_____
Date

🏃 MY FITNESS
Exercise

✝ MY TRUTH
Scripture Memory Verse

LIVE IT TRACKER

_____
_____
_____

MOOD

_____
_____

MOOD

_____
_____
_____
_____

MOOD

GROUP	FRUITS	VEGETABLES	GRAINS	PROTEIN	DAIRY	HEALTHY OILS & OTHER FATS	WATER & SUPER BEVERAGES
Estimate Total							

What made me happy today?

What positive step did I take for my health?

What intentional step will I take for tomorrow?

Celebrate
—— EVERY ——
VICTORY

_____/_____/_____
Date

🏃 MY FITNESS
Exercise

✝ MY TRUTH
Scripture Memory Verse

LIVE IT TRACKER

_____
_____
_____
_____

MOOD

_____
_____
_____

MOOD 😊 ☹ 😐

_____
_____
_____

MOOD 😊 ☹ 😐

GROUP	FRUITS	VEGETABLES	GRAINS	PROTEIN	DAIRY	HEALTHY OILS & OTHER FATS	WATER & SUPER BEVERAGES
Estimate Total							

What made me happy today?

What positive step did I take for my health?

What intentional step will I take for tomorrow?

_When God gives you a
new beginning,
don't repeat the
old mistakes_

_____/_____/_____
Date

MY FITNESS
Exercise

_____

_____

_____

✝ MY TRUTH
Scripture Memory Verse

_____

_____

_____

_____

LIVE IT TRACKER

_____

_____

MOOD

_____

_____

_____

MOOD

_____

_____

_____

MOOD

GROUP	FRUITS	VEGETABLES	GRAINS	PROTEIN	DAIRY	HEALTHY OILS & OTHER FATS	WATER & SUPER BEVERAGES
Estimate Total							

What made me happy today?

What positive step did I take for my health?

What intentional step will I take for tomorrow?

_____/_____/_____
Date

MY FITNESS
Exercise

✝ **MY TRUTH**
Scripture Memory Verse

LIVE IT TRACKER

MOOD

MOOD 😊 🙁 😐

MOOD 😊 🙁 😐

GROUP	FRUITS	VEGETABLES	GRAINS	PROTEIN	DAIRY	HEALTHY OILS & OTHER FATS	WATER & SUPER BEVERAGES
Estimate Total							

What made me happy today?

What positive step did I take for my health?

What intentional step will I take for tomorrow?

It's About PROGRESS Not Perfection

_____/_____/_____

Date

MY FITNESS
Exercise

_____

_____

_____

✝ **MY TRUTH**
Scripture Memory Verse

_____

_____

_____

_____

LIVE IT TRACKER

_____

_____

_____

MOOD

_____

_____

_____

MOOD

_____

_____

_____

MOOD

GROUP	FRUITS	VEGETABLES	GRAINS	PROTEIN	DAIRY	HEALTHY OILS & OTHER FATS	WATER & SUPER BEVERAGES
Estimate Total							

What made me happy today?

What positive step did I take for my health?

What intentional step will I take for tomorrow?

THE
ONLY BAD
WORKOUT
IS THE ONE
YOU DIDN'T DO

_____/_____/_____

Date

MY FITNESS
Exercise

_____

_____

_____

✝ MY TRUTH
Scripture Memory Verse

_____

_____

_____

_____

MY NUTRITION

_____

_____

_____

MOOD ☺ ☹ 😐

_____

_____

_____

MOOD ☺ ☹ 😐

_____

_____

_____

MOOD ☺ ☹ 😐

GROUP	FRUITS	VEGETABLES	GRAINS	PROTEIN	DAIRY	HEALTHY OILS & OTHER FATS	WATER & SUPER BEVERAGES
Estimate Total							

What made me happy today?

What positive step did I take for my health?

What intentional step will I take for tomorrow?

GREATER IS HE
that is in you
THAN HE THAT IS
in the world.

1 JOHN 4:4

_____ / _____ / _____

Date

MY FITNESS
Exercise

_____

_____

_____

✝ # MY TRUTH
Scripture Memory Verse

_____

_____

_____

_____

LIVE IT TRACKER

_____

_____

_____

_____

MOOD

_____

_____

_____

_____

MOOD

_____

_____

_____

_____

MOOD

GROUP	FRUITS	VEGETABLES	GRAINS	PROTEIN	DAIRY	HEALTHY OILS & OTHER FATS	WATER & SUPER BEVERAGES
Estimate Total							

What made me happy today?

What positive step did I take for my health?

What intentional step will I take for tomorrow?

Small steps
lead to
big changes

_____/_____/_____
Date

MY FITNESS
Exercise

_____

_____

_____

MY TRUTH
Scripture Memory Verse

_____

_____

_____

_____

LIVE IT TRACKER

_____

_____

_____

MOOD 🙂 🙁 😐

_____

_____

_____

MOOD 🙂 🙁 😐

_____

_____

_____

MOOD 🙂 🙁 😐

GROUP	FRUITS	VEGETABLES	GRAINS	PROTEIN	DAIRY	HEALTHY OILS & OTHER FATS	WATER & SUPER BEVERAGES
Estimate Total							

What made me happy today?

What positive step did I take for my health?

What intentional step will I take for tomorrow?

_____

_____

_____

_____

_____

_____

_____

_____

_____

_____

_____

_____

_____

_____

_____

_____

_____

_____

_____

_____

_____

_____

_____

_____

Made in the USA
Coppell, TX
12 July 2020